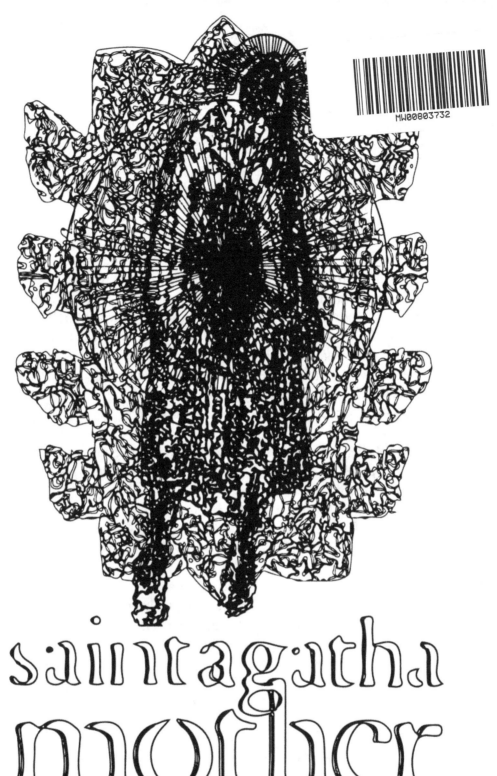

saintagatha
mother
redeemer
a coloring book

michèle saint-michel

MW00803732

Copyright © 2022 Michèle Saint-Michel
All rights reserved.
10 9 8 7 6 5 4 3 2 1

Published by Bad Saturn. BAD SATURN and associated
logos are trademarks and/ or registered trademarks.

All rights reserved under International and Pan-American
Copyright Conventions. No part of this publication may be
reproduced, transmitted, downloaded, decompiled, reverse
engineered, or stored in or introduced into any information
storage and retrieval system, in any form or by any means,
whether electronic or mechanical, now known or hereafter
invented, without the express written permission of the
publisher. For information regarding permissions, email
Bad Saturn, Attention: Permissions Department.

The publisher does not have any control over and does not
assume any responsibility for author or third-party websites
or their content.

LIBRARY OF CONGRESS
CATALOGING-IN-PUBLICATION DATA

Saint-Michel, Michèle.
Saint Agatha Mother Redeemer Coloring Book
/ by Michèle Saint-Michel.
— 1st ed.
p.
Crn.
ISBN: 978-0-9999020-2-8

Summary:
Using layered imagery, text messages, and illustrated
self-portraiture, Saint Agatha Mother Redeemer takes you on a
journey through the unsteady waters of healing after traumatic
events and living with PTSD. The Saint Agatha Mother Redeemer
Coloring Book features outlined illustrations from the original
book that are ready to be brought to living color with
your favorite colored pencils, crayons, or markers.

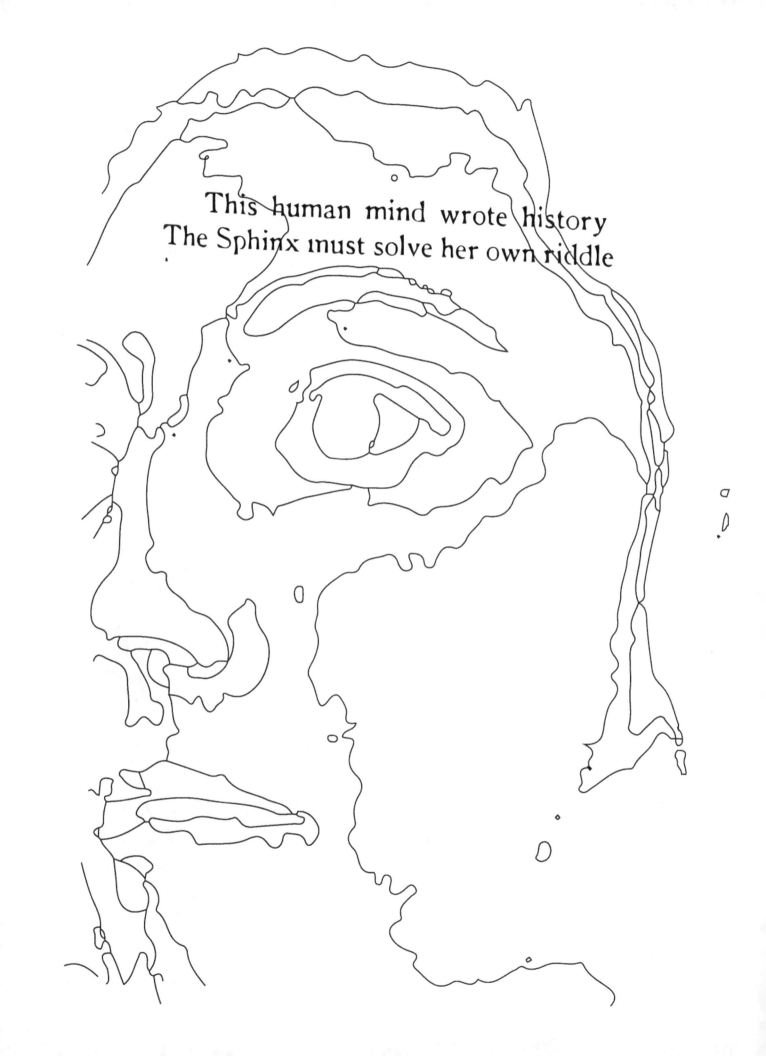

This human mind wrote history
The Sphinx must solve her own riddle

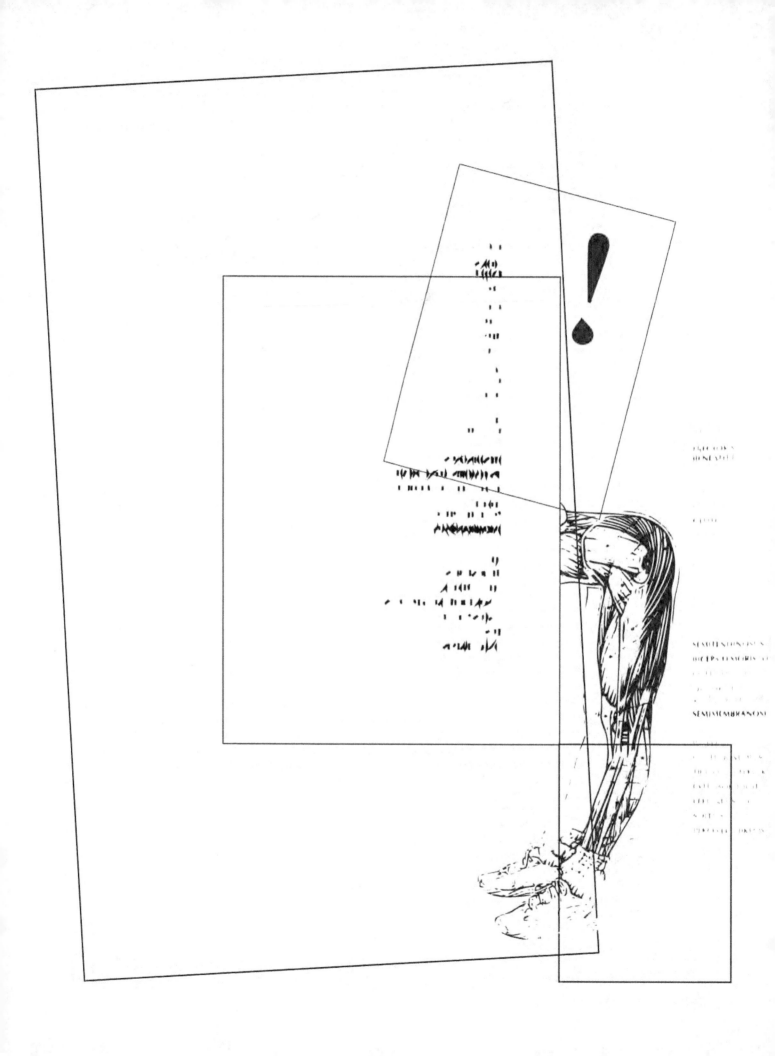

good enough for a real carcass treat

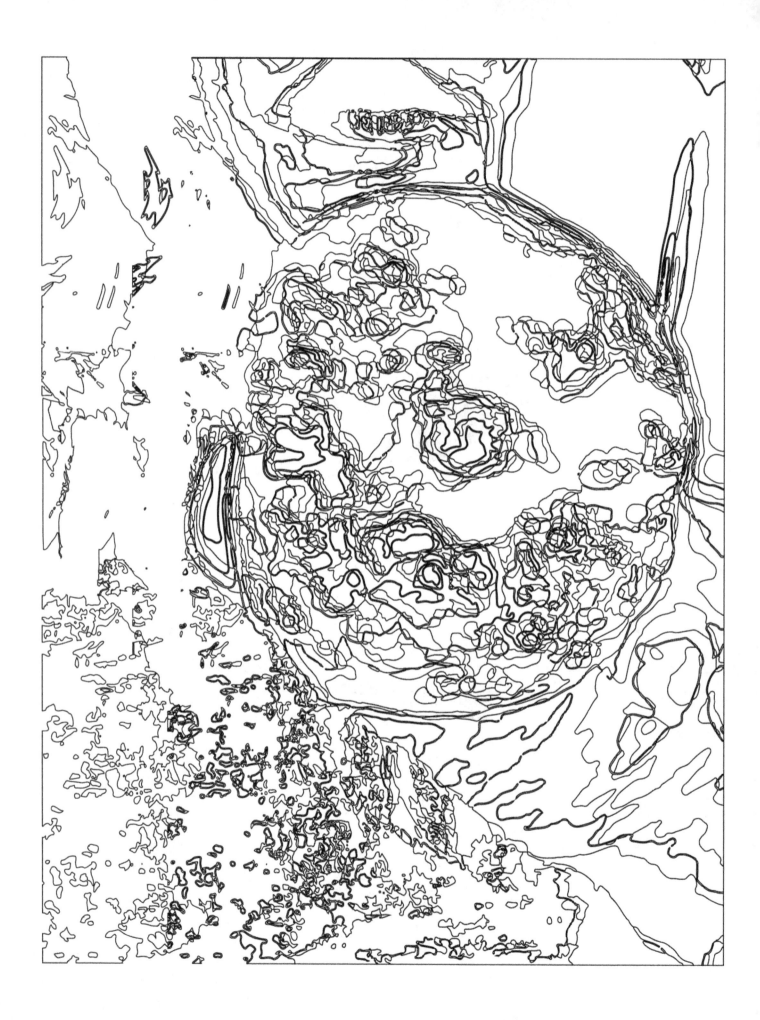

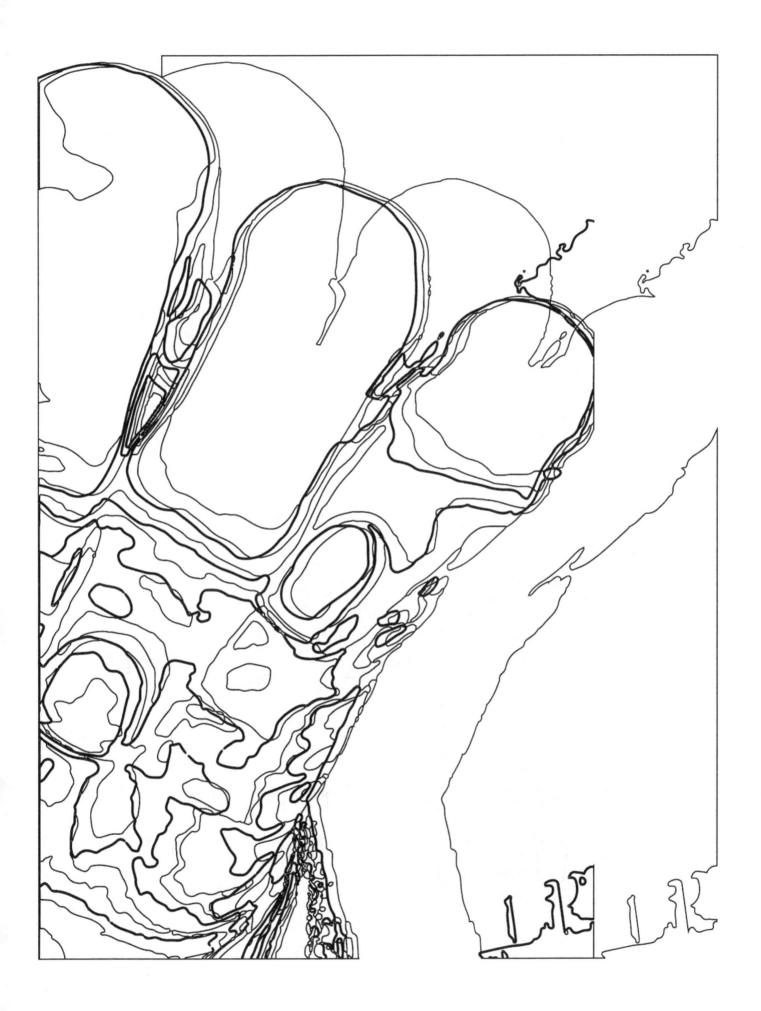

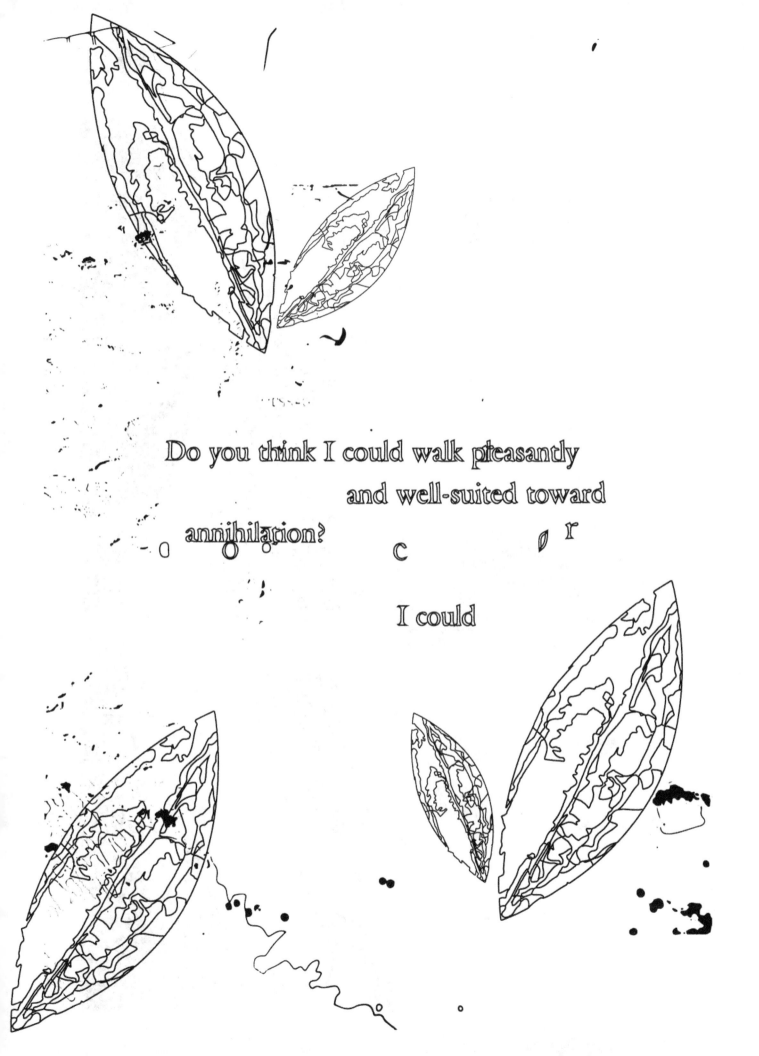

Do you think I could walk pleasantly
and well-suited toward
annihilation?
o
o o c o r

I could

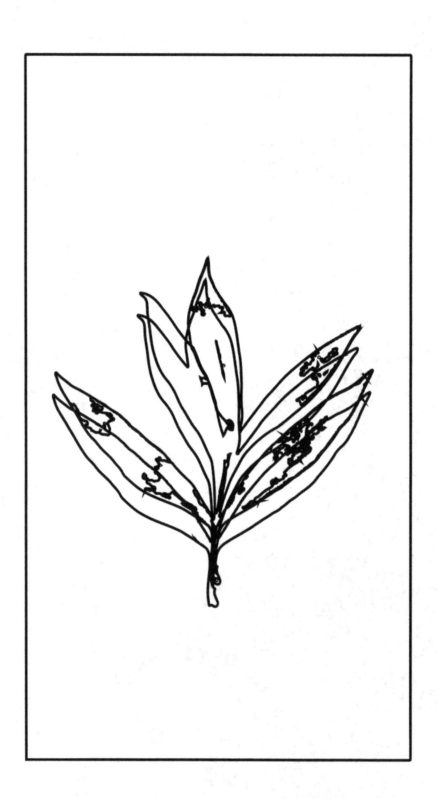

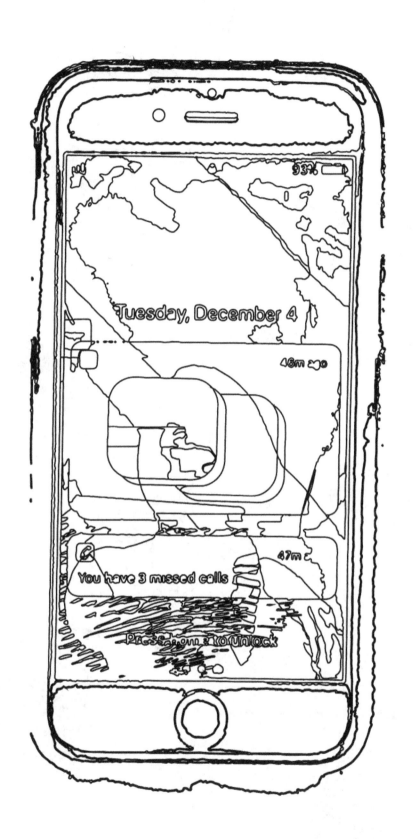

Chats

Chats

Lists	New

Tap for more nfo   21 20 >

You were   Monday →

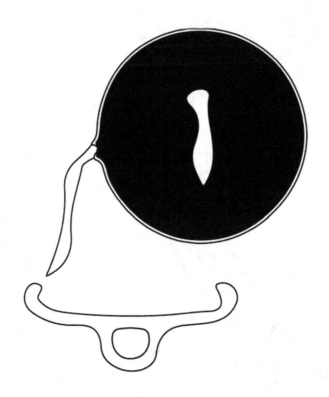

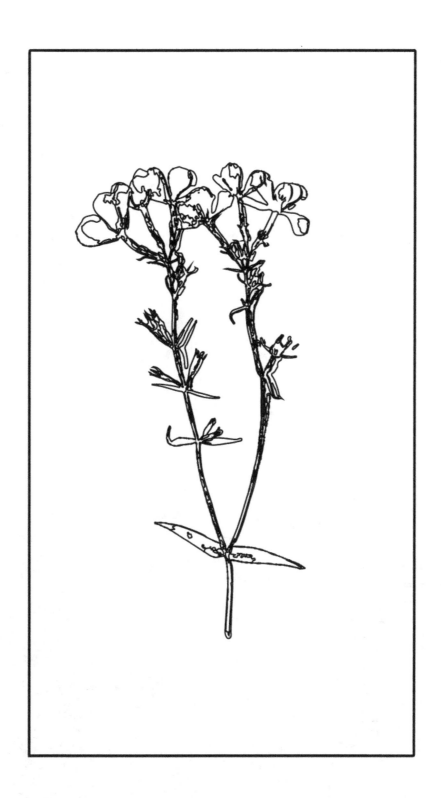

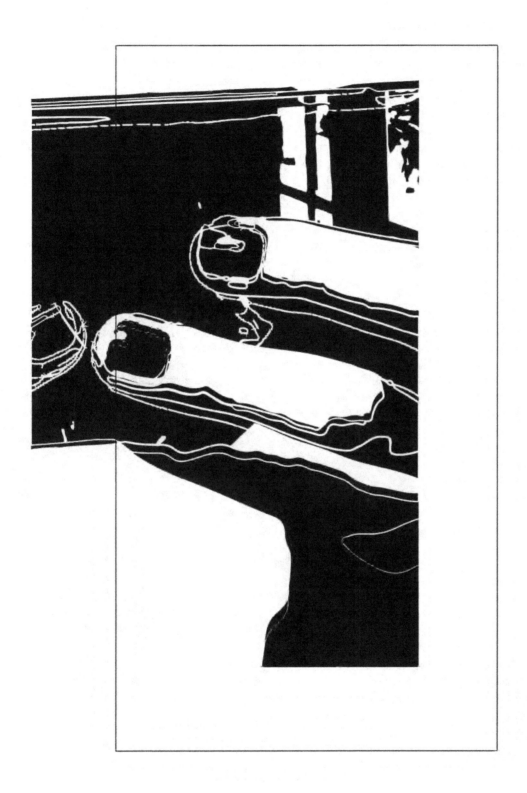

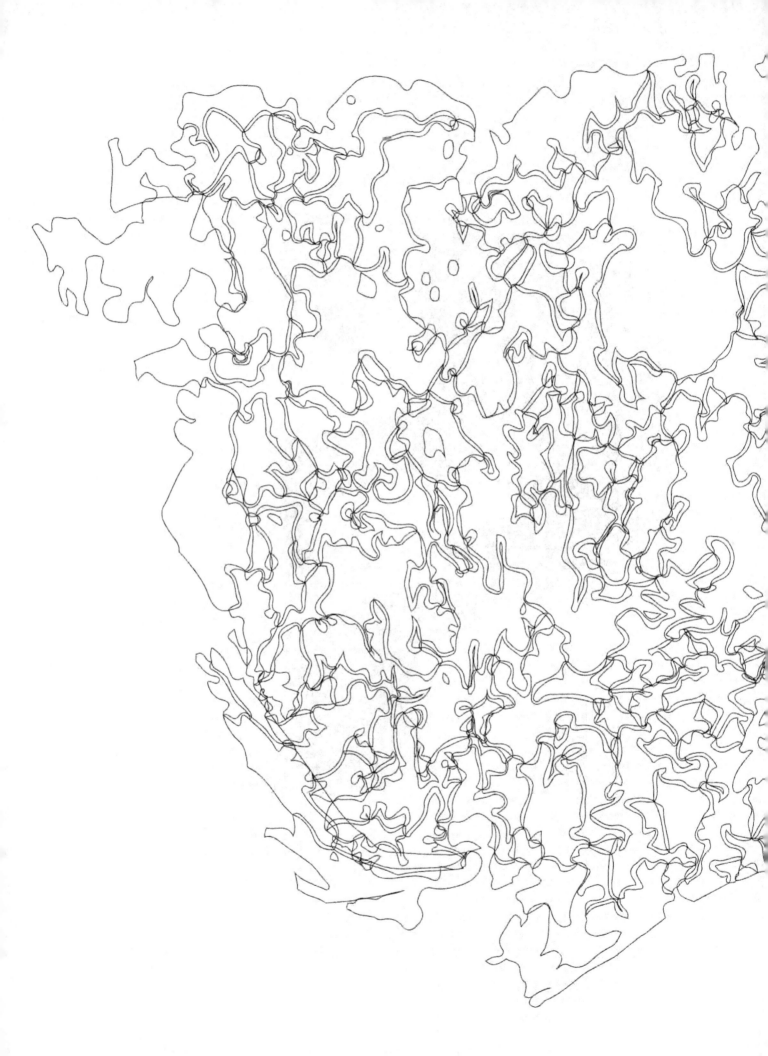

looking at the movements of the
stars, I can't picture to myself
the rotation of the earth,
                          and I'm right
.
in saying that the stars move
          ''A d   ld h

theloop•moosttwi·g·oofthe·birc-h-tre--e

What is behind me
Rand puts to sco y a
ta isagod md slhassis finy
long-threaded moss fruits,

ds, and birds all over,
nd me for good reasons,
h desire it

Lines Composed a Few Miles
and fathomless as myself;
They do not know how immortal,
but I know.

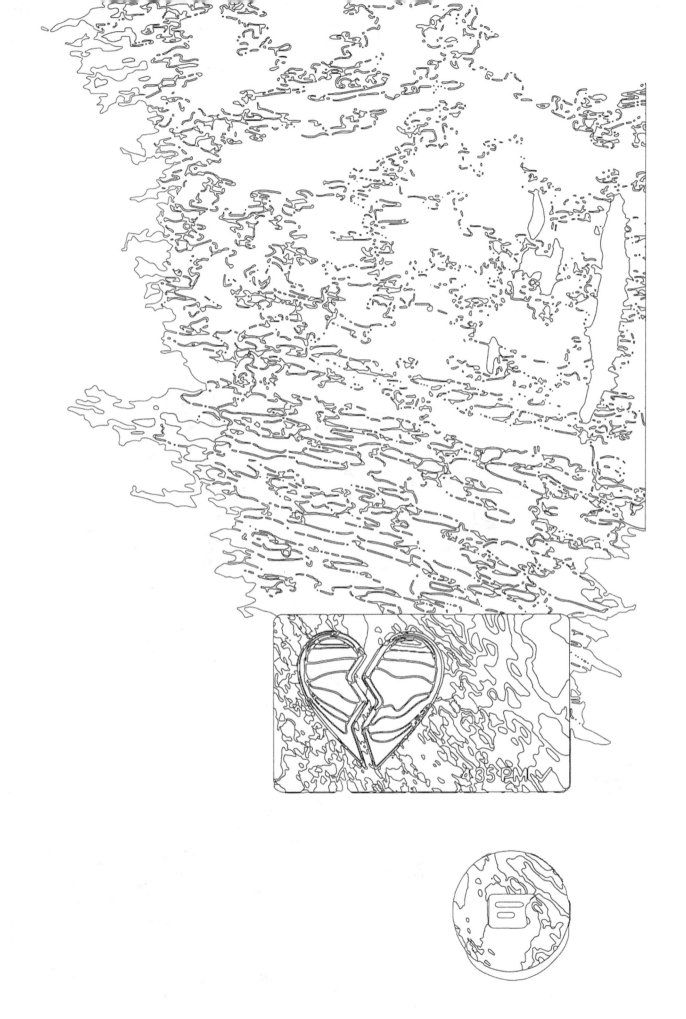

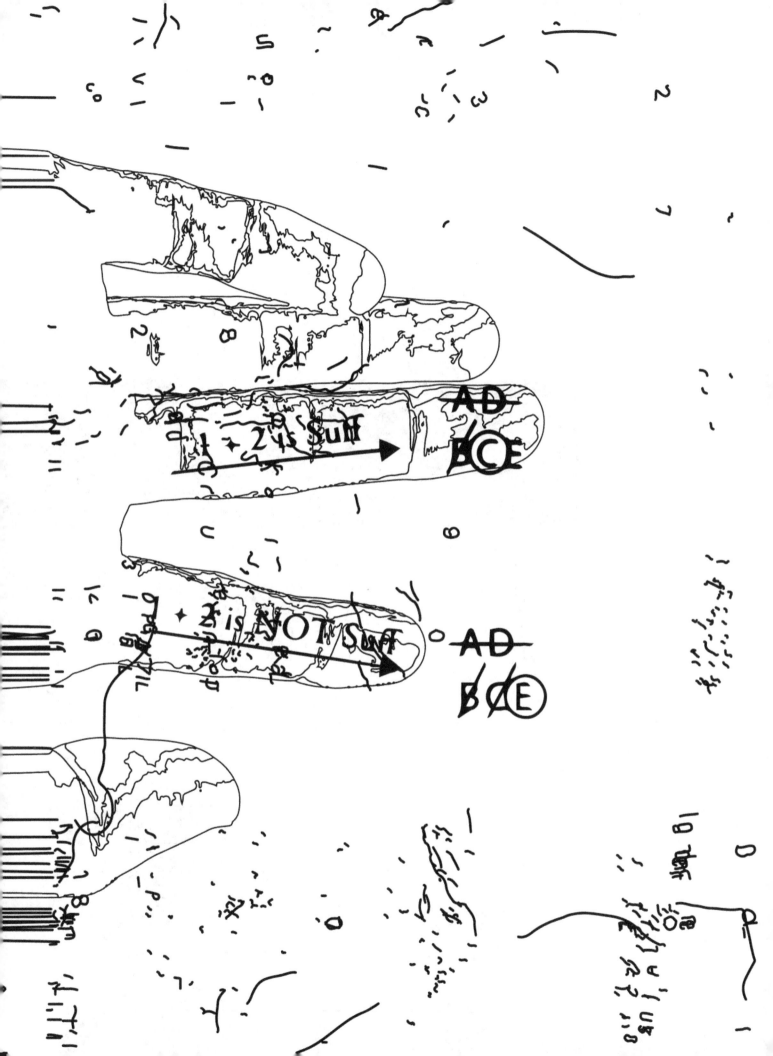

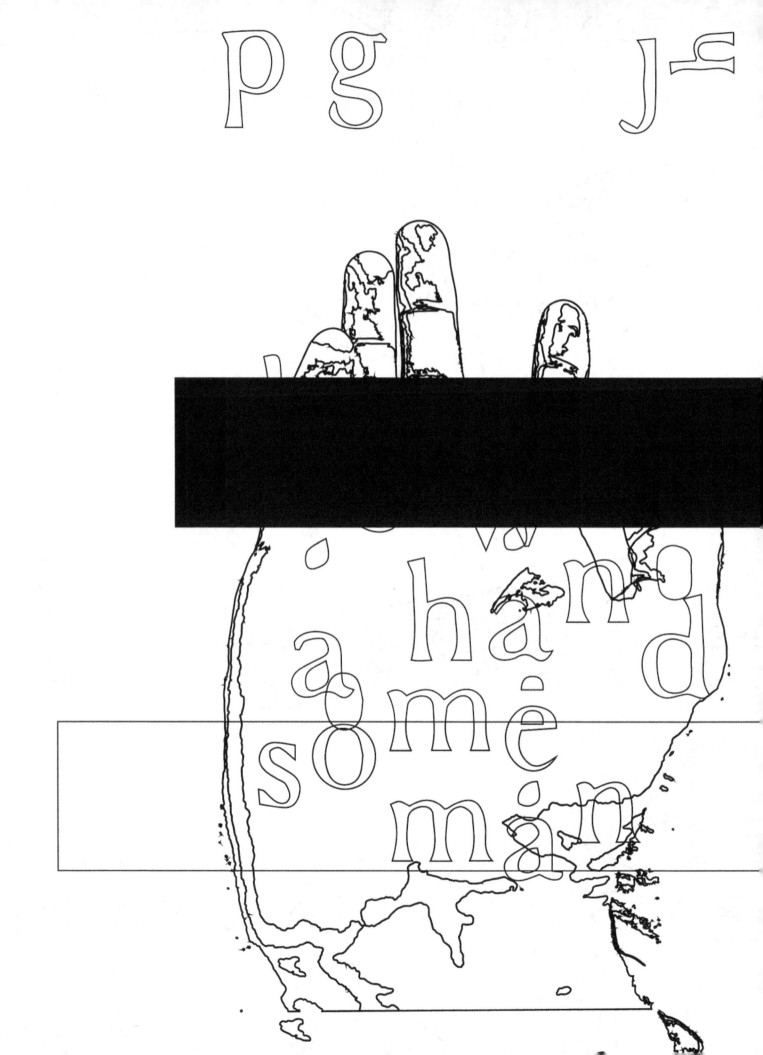

ethat

us

gentle

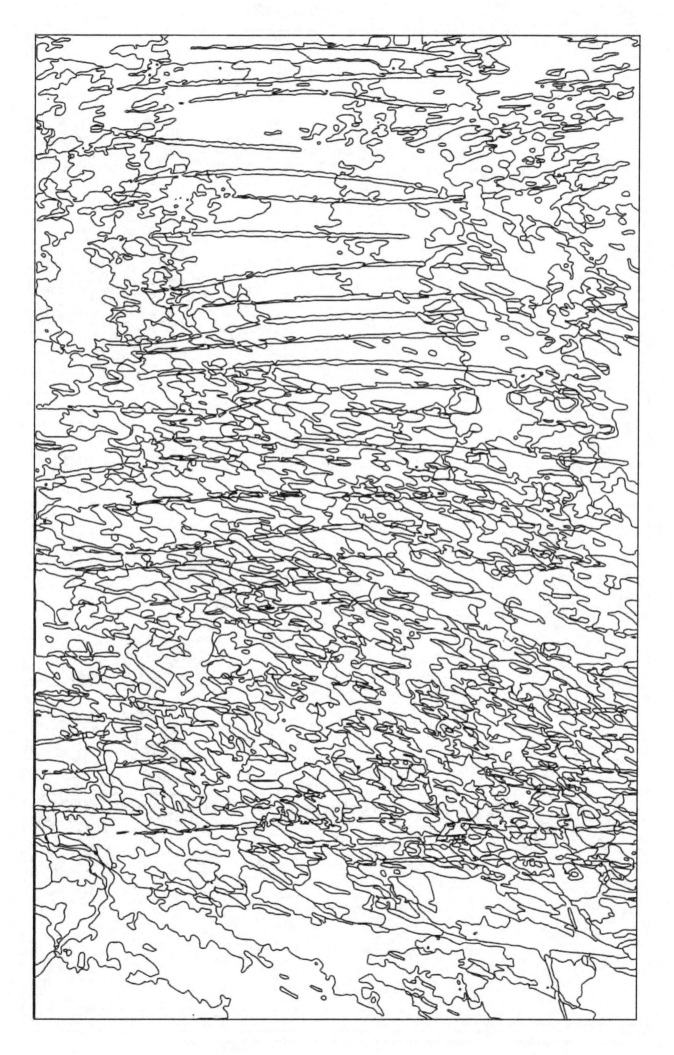

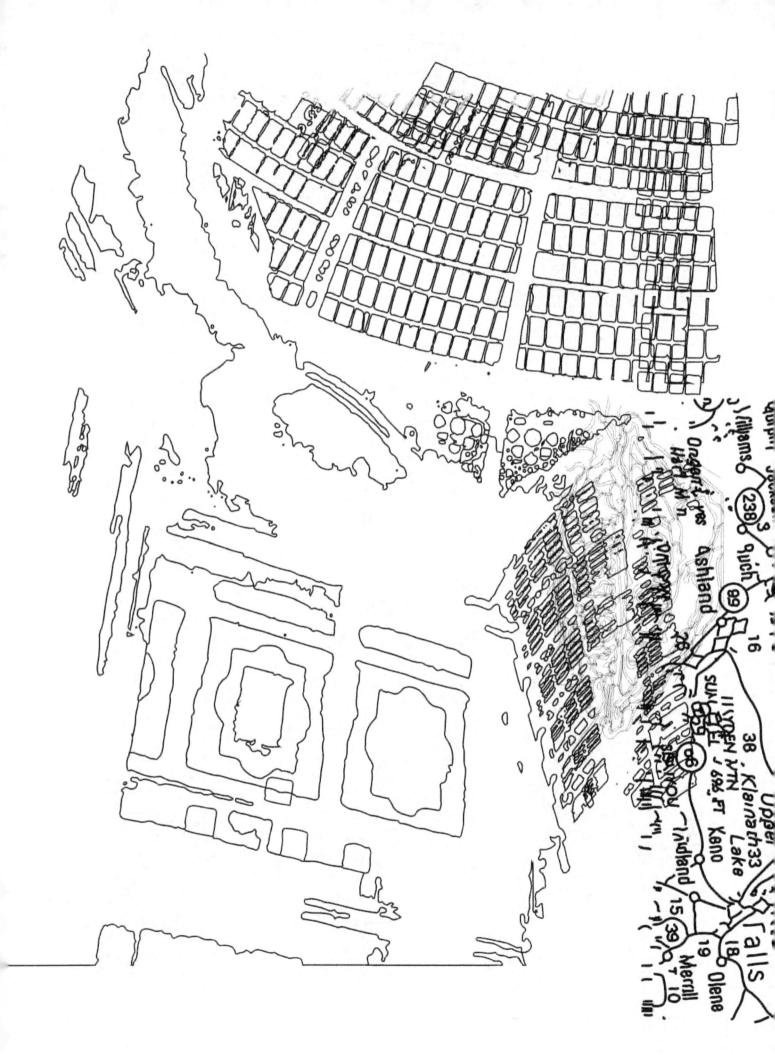

ut, adorned with green dock
appeared as splendidly and
ll those rare and foreign in
them. Then were the gener
ple and sincere expressions
ceived, without seeking artif
ad fraud, deceit, and malic
Justice maintained her pro
favor and interest, which nov
e her. Law was not yet left
en there was neither cause nor
re, went about alone, without
om and lewd designs of other
y owing to their own natural i
stable ages of ours, no damse
nclosed in another labyrinth
h some cranny, or through
the amours pestilence find e
ite of all seclusion. Therefore
ncreased, to defend maidens,
ns and persons distressed, t

behold the
picturesque giant

and stop there,
stop
and stop there,
and stop there,
and stop there,
and stop there
and stop the

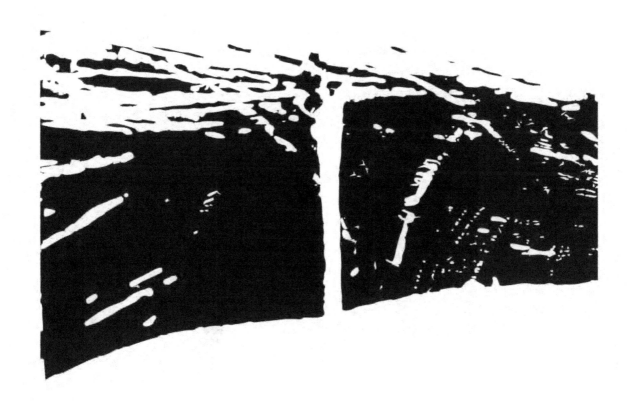

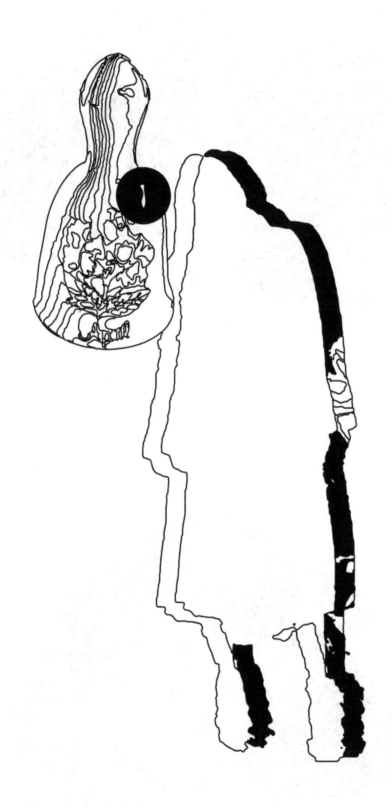

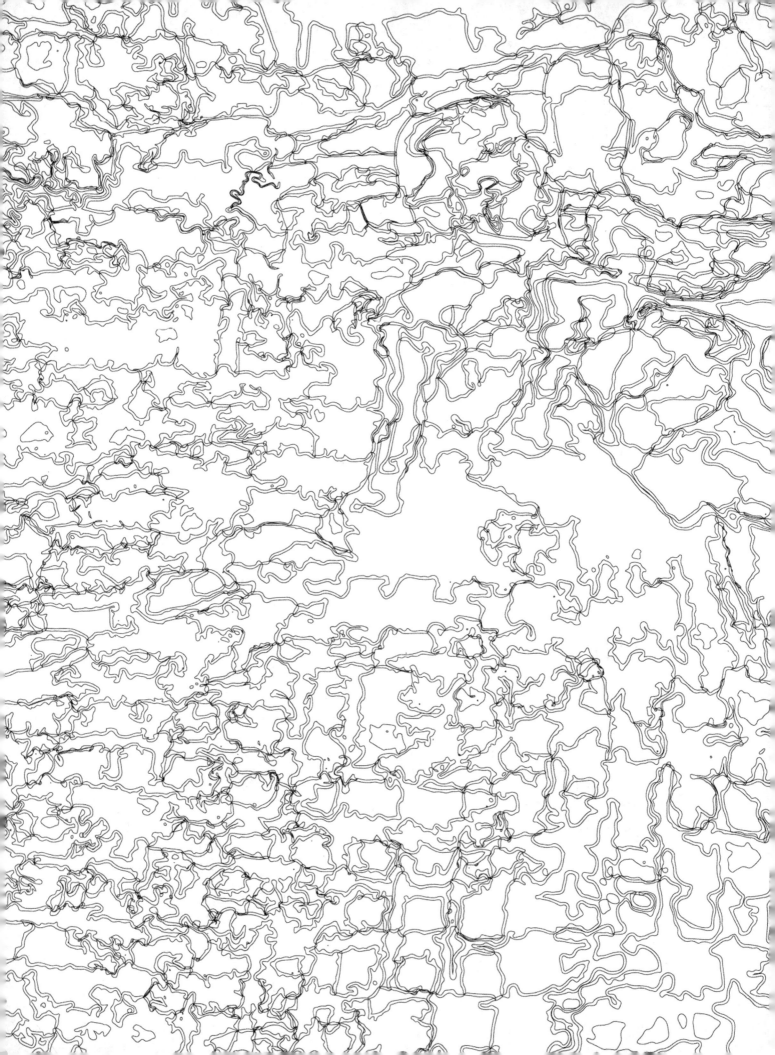

And do
not call
the
tortoise

it chy?
ch i much
ch

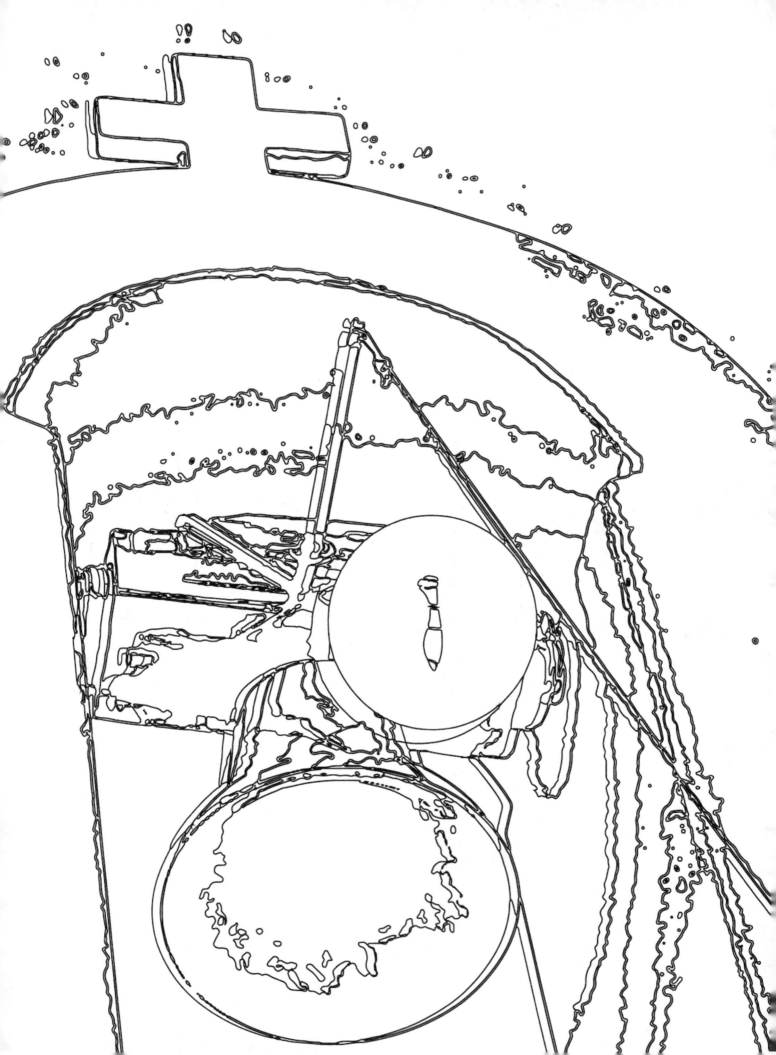

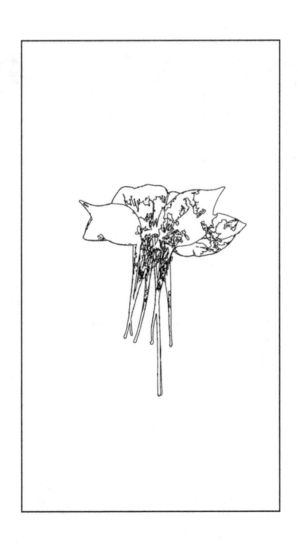

agnus dei

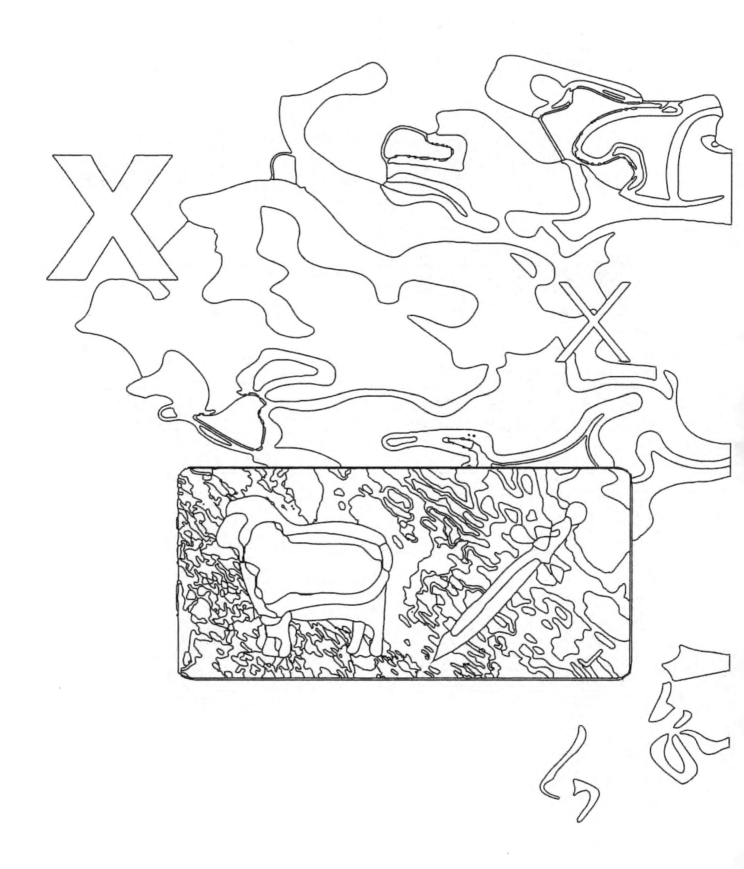

Adhaesit pavimento anima mea

This human mind wrote history
The Sphinx must solve her own riddle

Be
pleasant!
a Swallow
remind my
whole!
Heart
Future, Head!
herb   time:
Present, be   And,
act
in Past
perspective,
Let   It
sands
illusion,
eyes.
world truly
mountain
looks
far
like
hidden. through
range   the
away, my all
leave but
enough   If
lives
strife not
no
behind
was

Trust men make us
God   bury us
within
o'erhead!

Act, dead
sublime, the
were howe'er
living
Footprints
great and
from how
departing

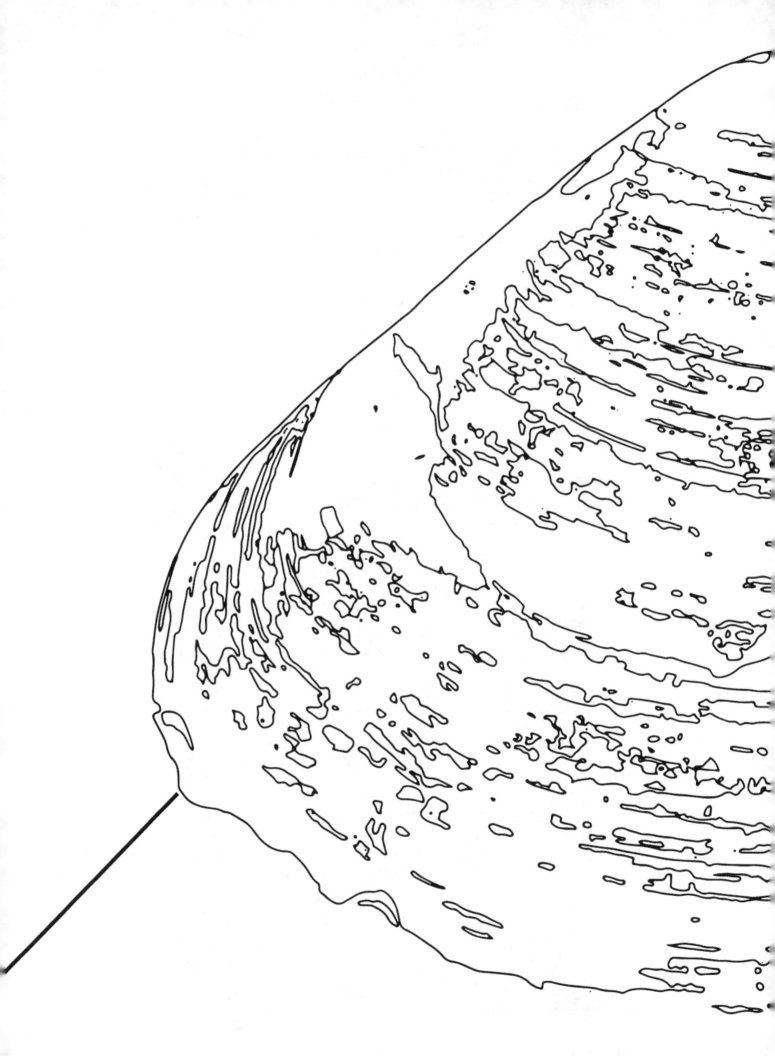

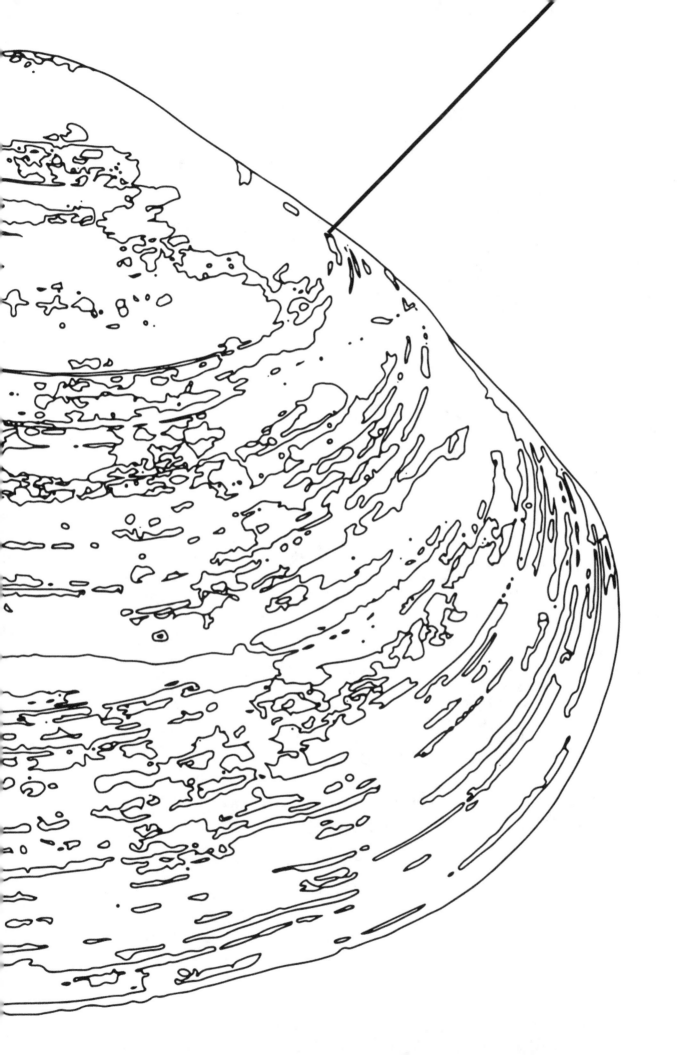

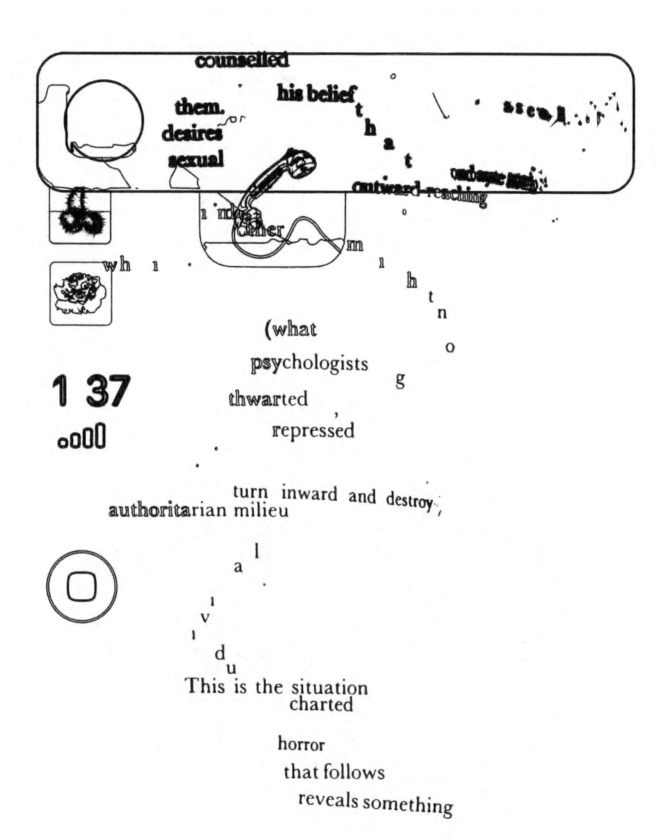

counselled

them.

desires

sexual

his belief

t
h
a
t

wh   i

(what

psychologists

thwarted

repressed

1 37

turn inward and destroy

authoritarian milieu

l
a

l
v
l
d
u

This is the situation

charted

horror

that follows

reveals something

I astonish more

than they?

' caresser

of life

how fast I run!

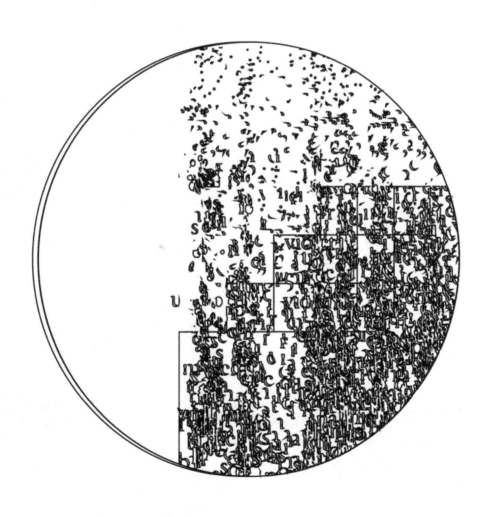

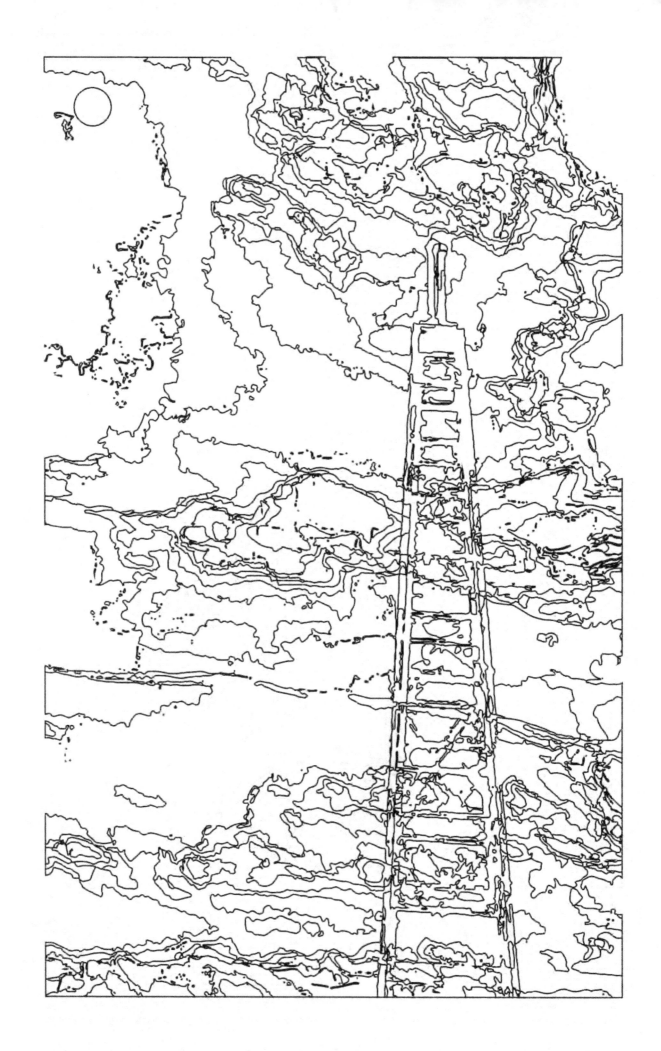

La morte della Xonnessione

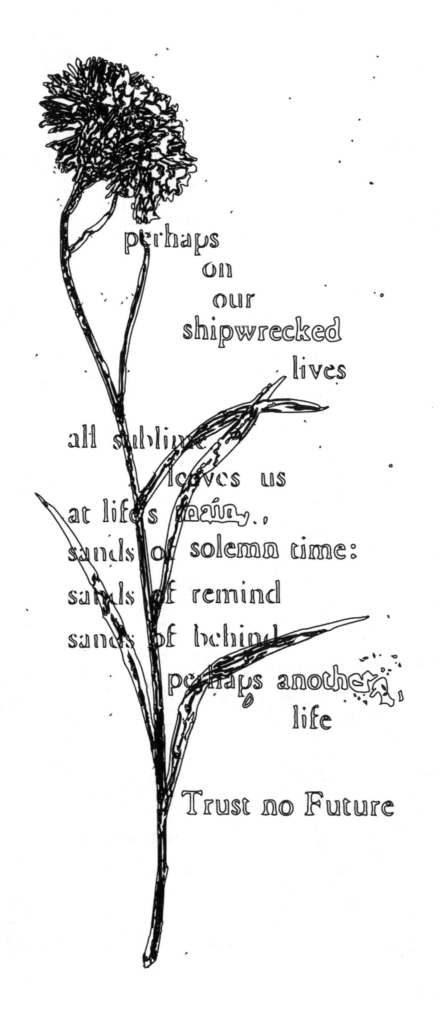

perhaps
on
our
shipwrecked
lives

all sublime
leaves us
at life's main,.
sands of solemn time:
sands of remind
sands of behind
perhaps another,
life

Trust no Future

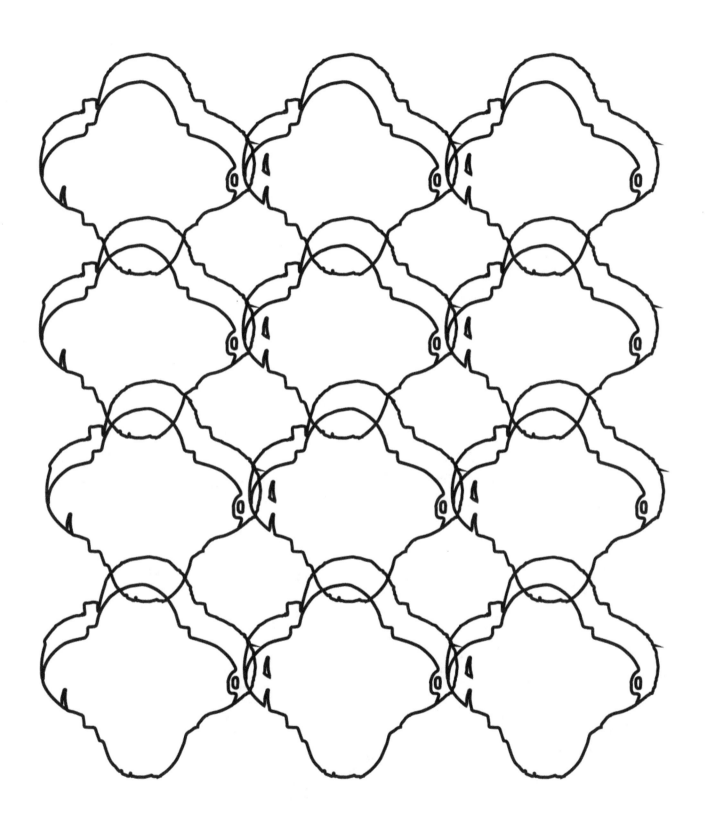

dv ssfxn g   f e enlgs

dmv ext fr   om   mm   eo

dr.cbcn   t ra tin g

rrd.éfi o as   e cm   eo hacv

r.s'nsth   as s we tin g .

rb antbaus a,   o r pe un rel

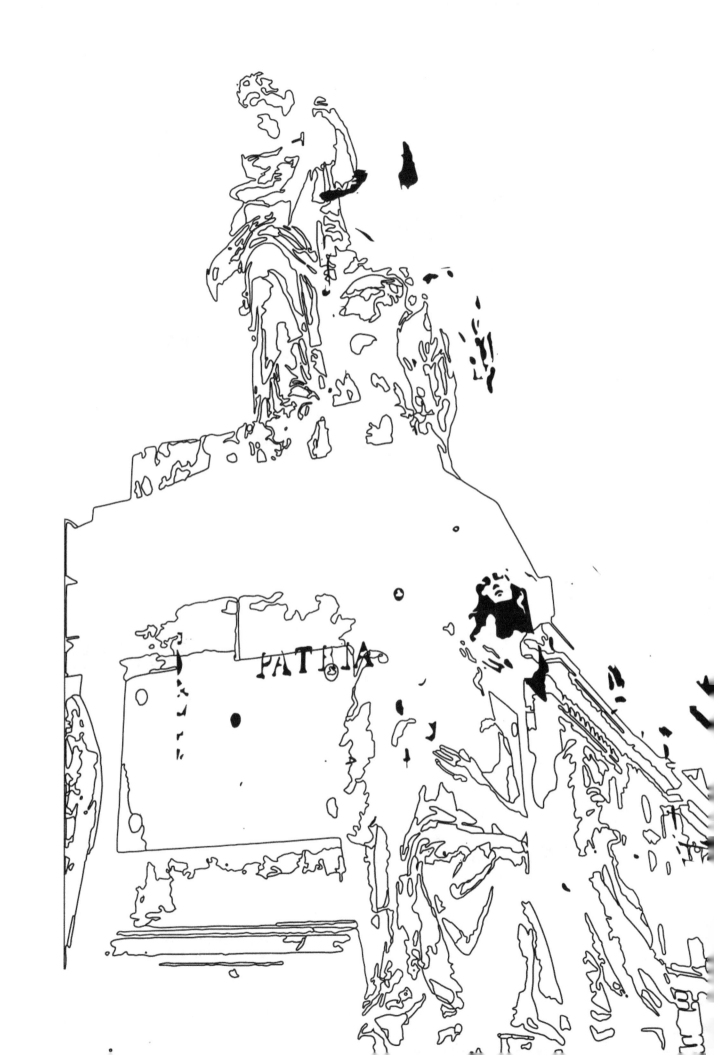

I began

        this violent fire

o pine-trees

          first bundles

began to melt

        dying.

, fire

, fire

I made them hurry

every man did

force; a load

a mild and gentle

tapestry and old cloth

pewter trees   A

year   it

to examine fire two of

from the rain. hand them

l alacrity, weighing

a butcher

dérègle-
ment de
tous les
sens

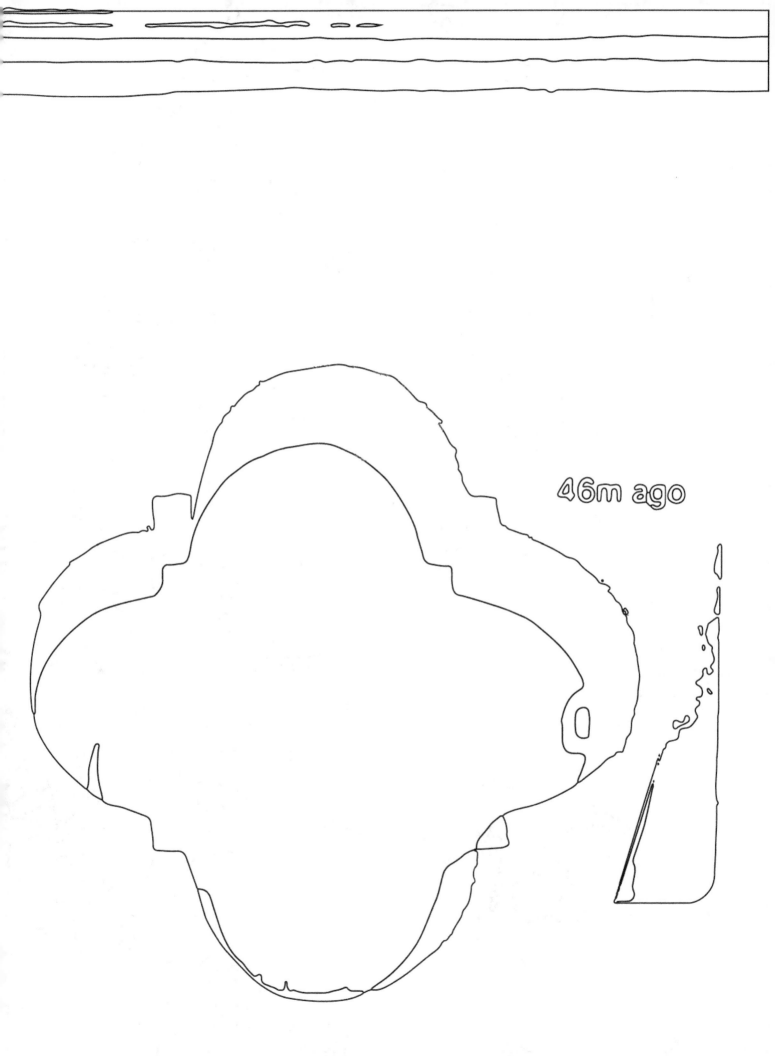

46m ago

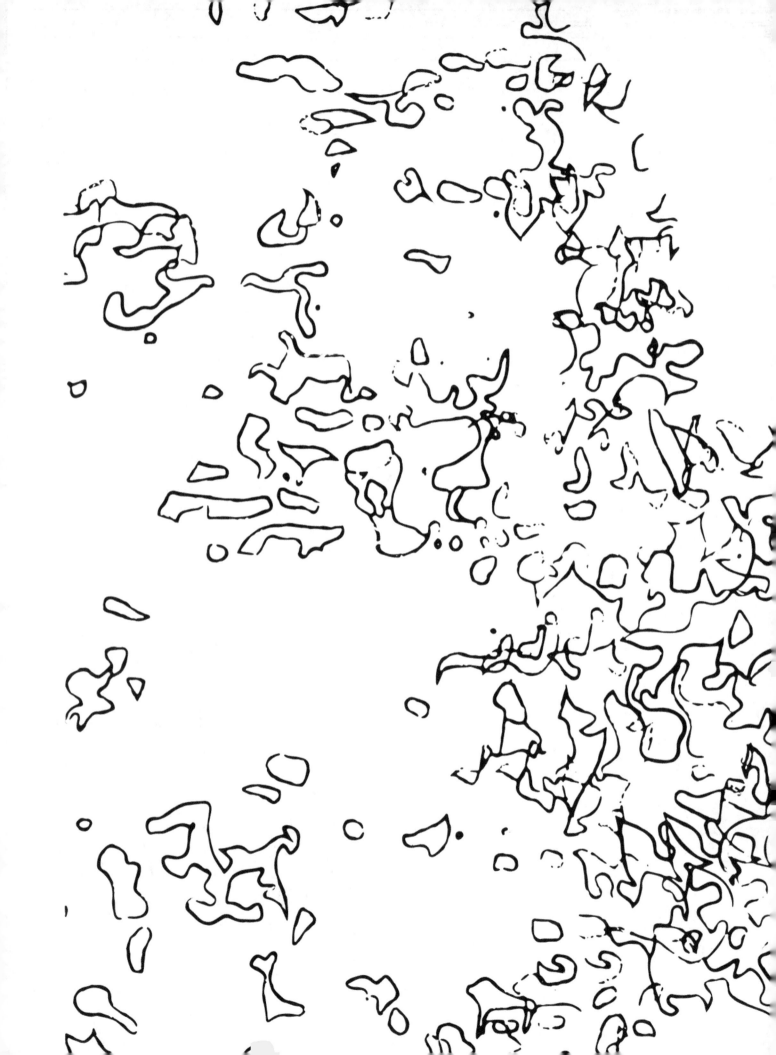

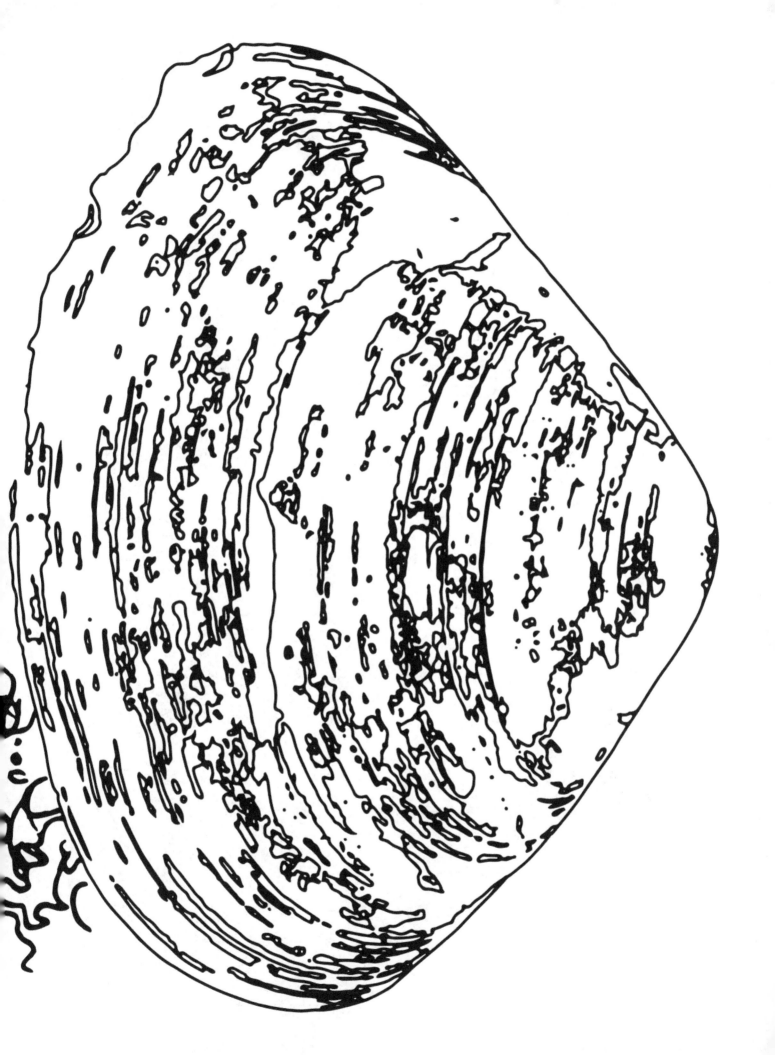

Turn SMS notifi-
cations off?

Location services have been turned off

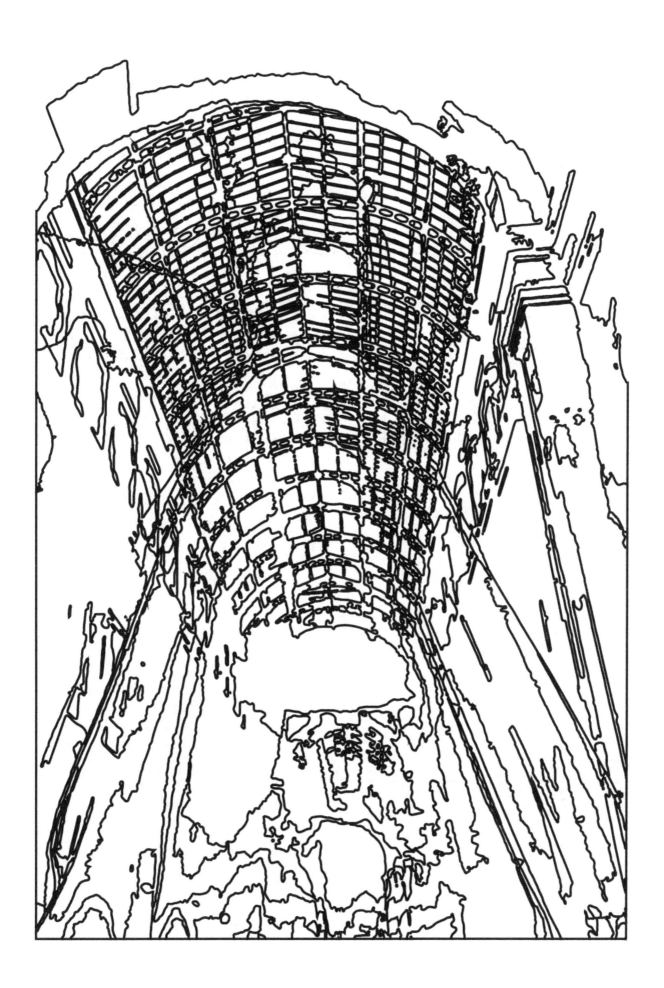

you see my heart, you know my de- sires

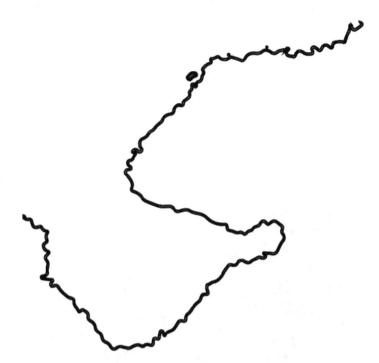

What is less
than a touch
nobody denies?
Only what
or more
is so.

possess

all I am

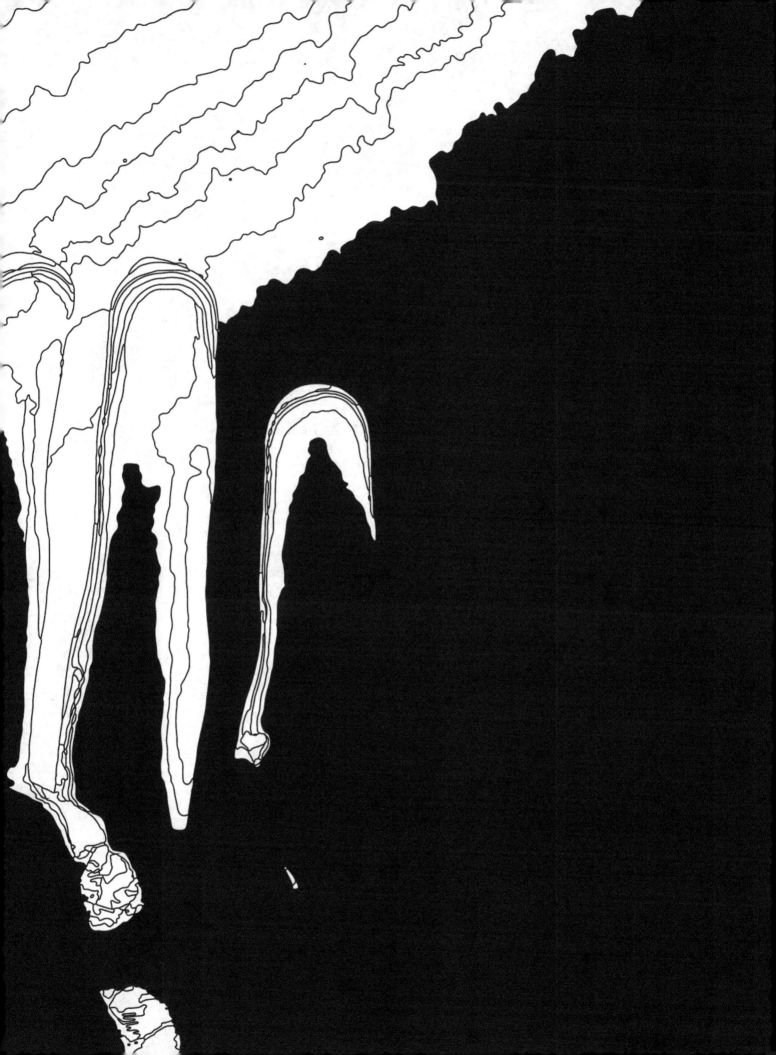

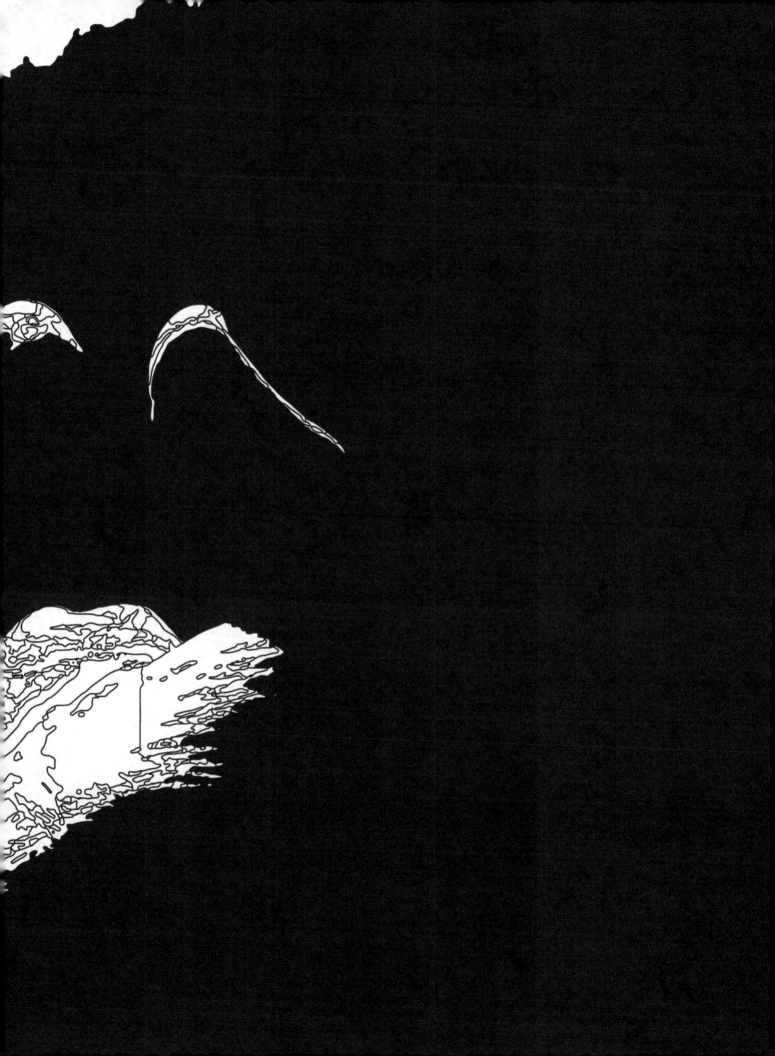

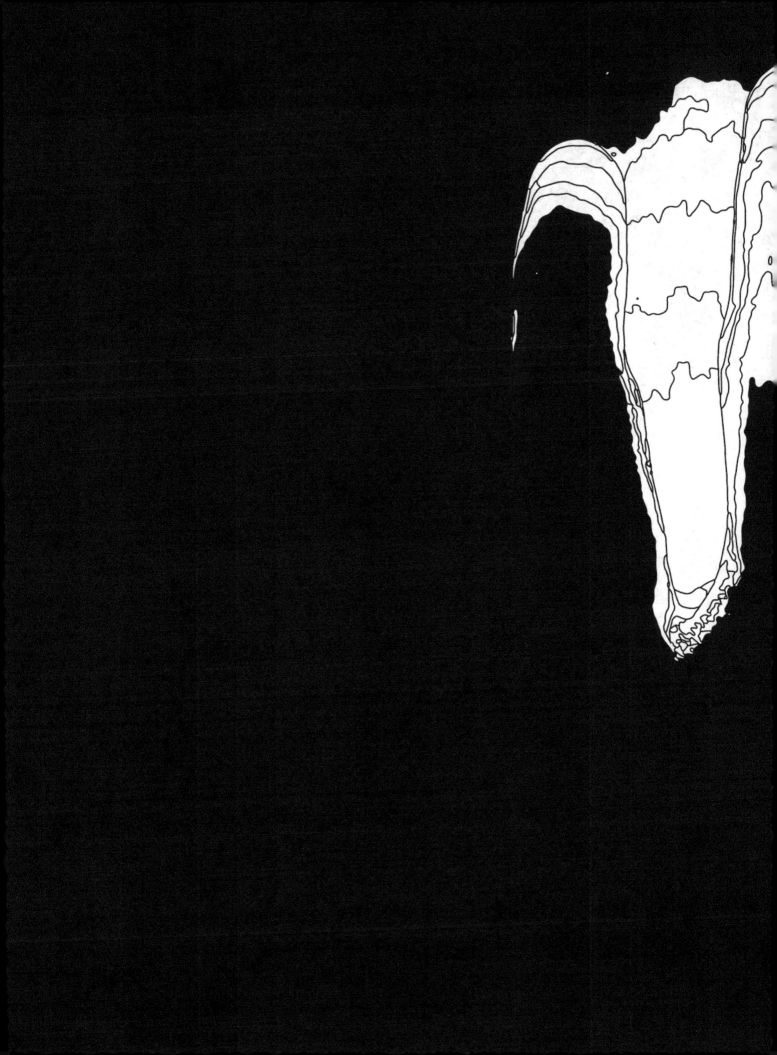

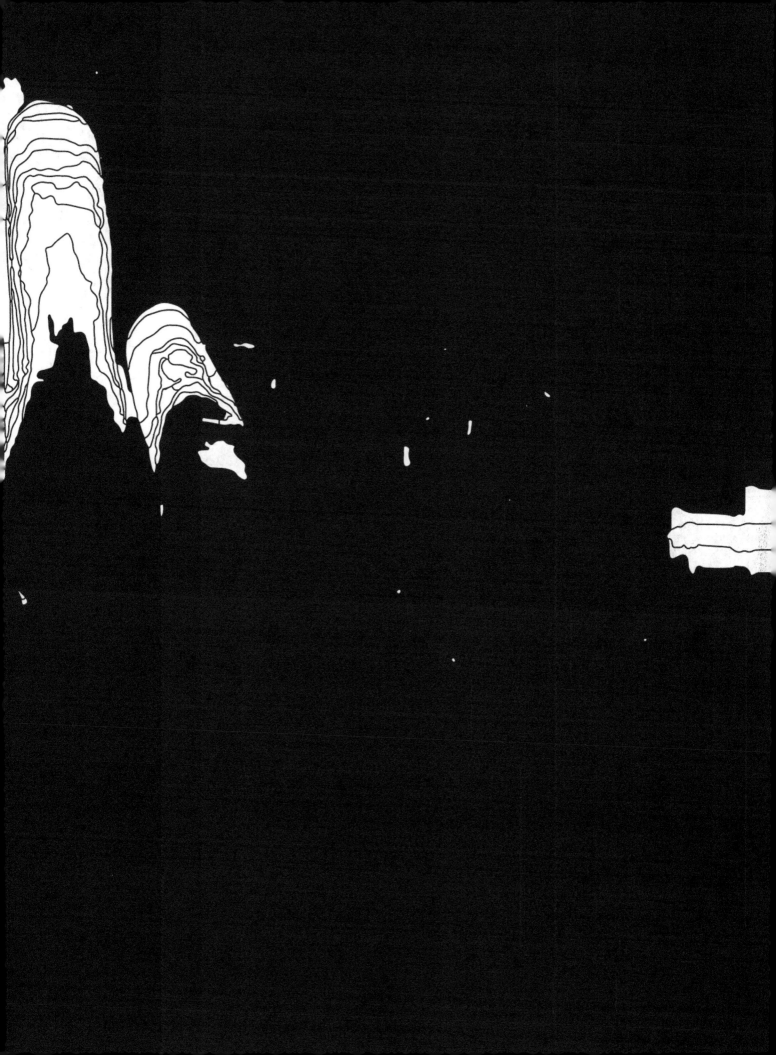

why did your pain feel tender?

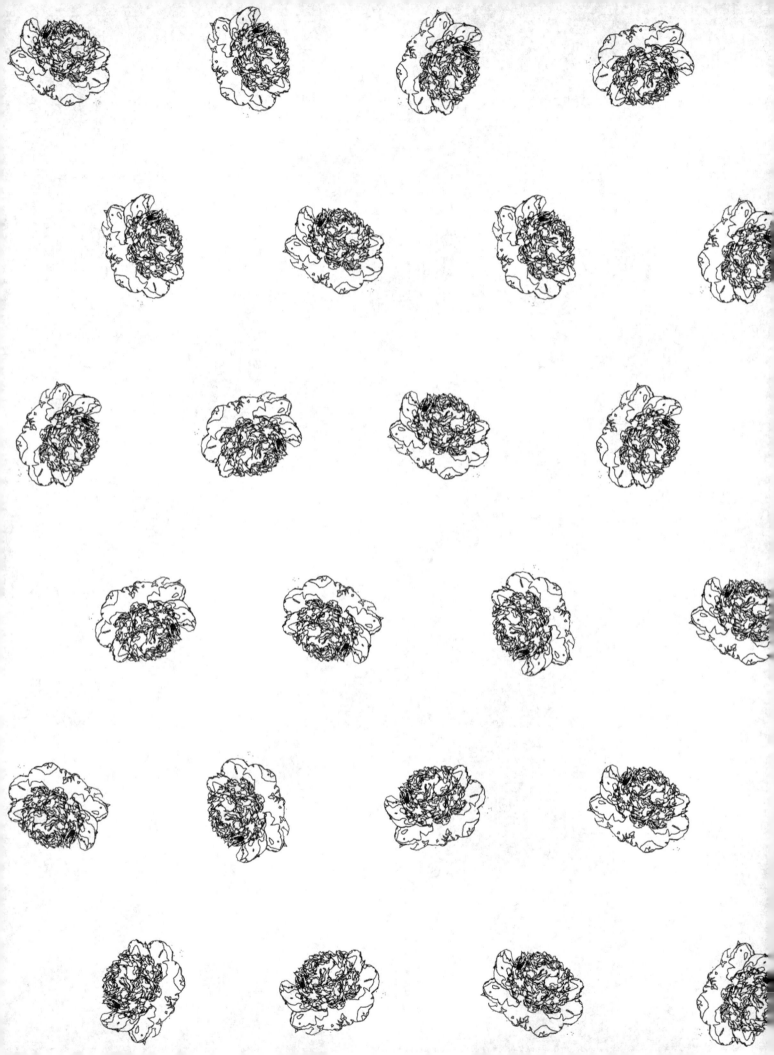

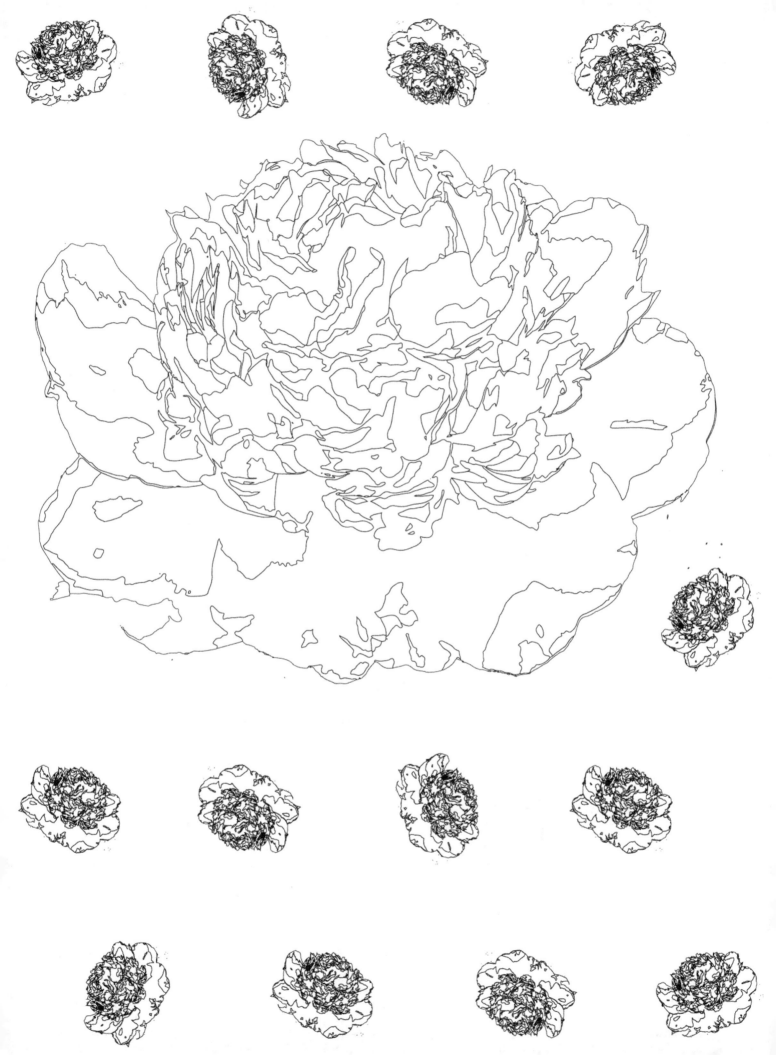

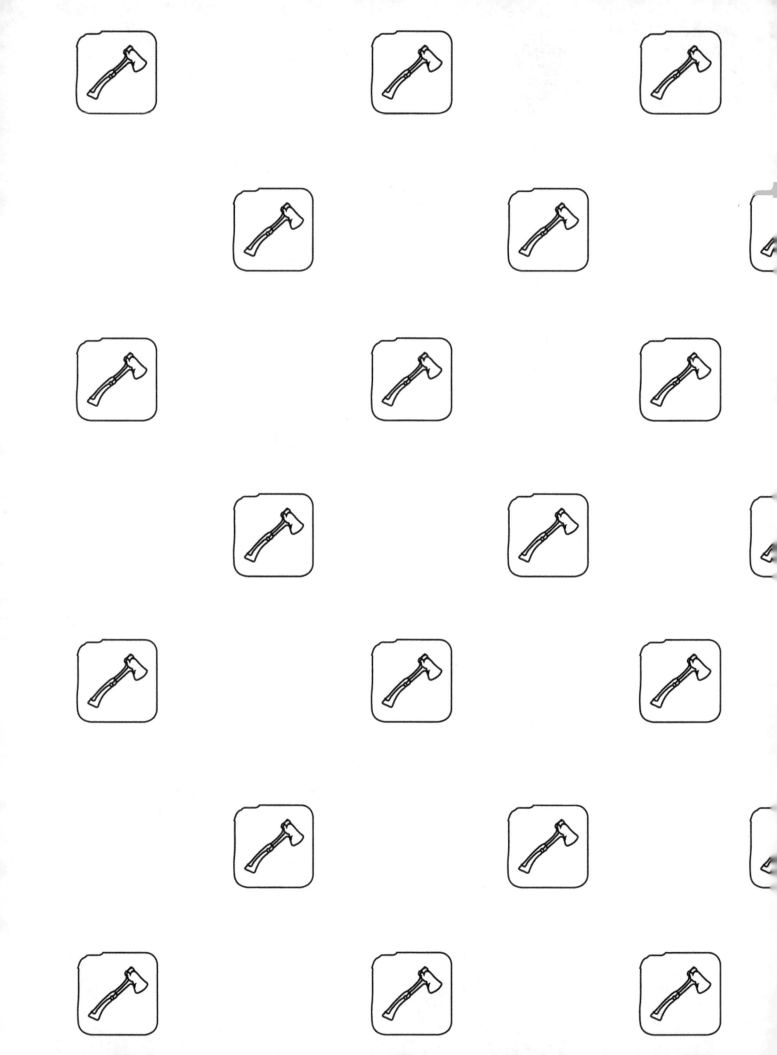

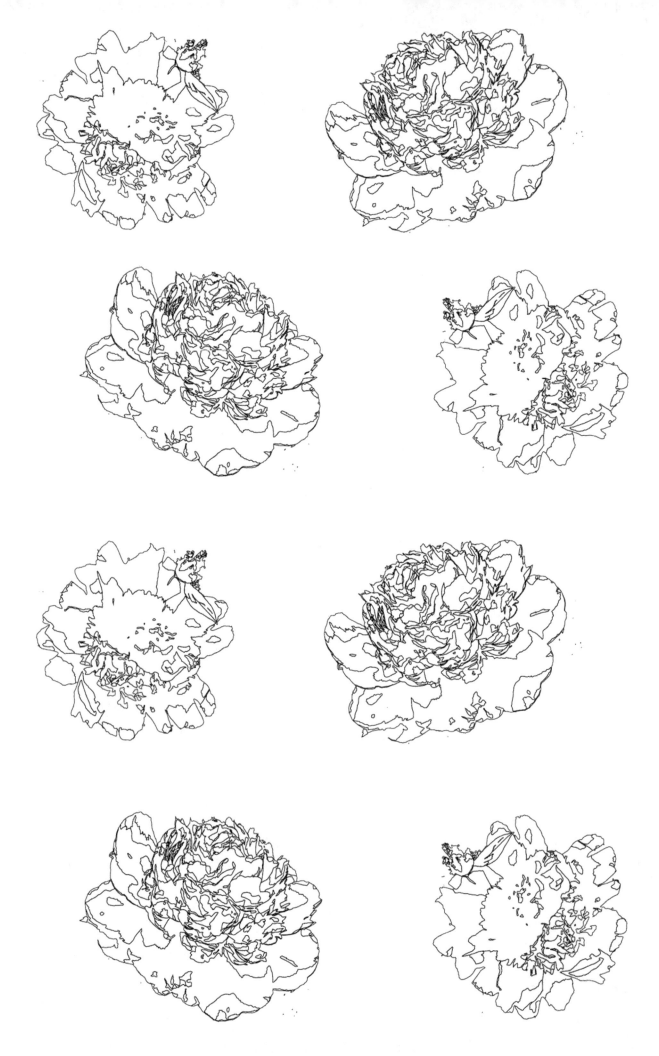

life appeared.

And ceased

the moment

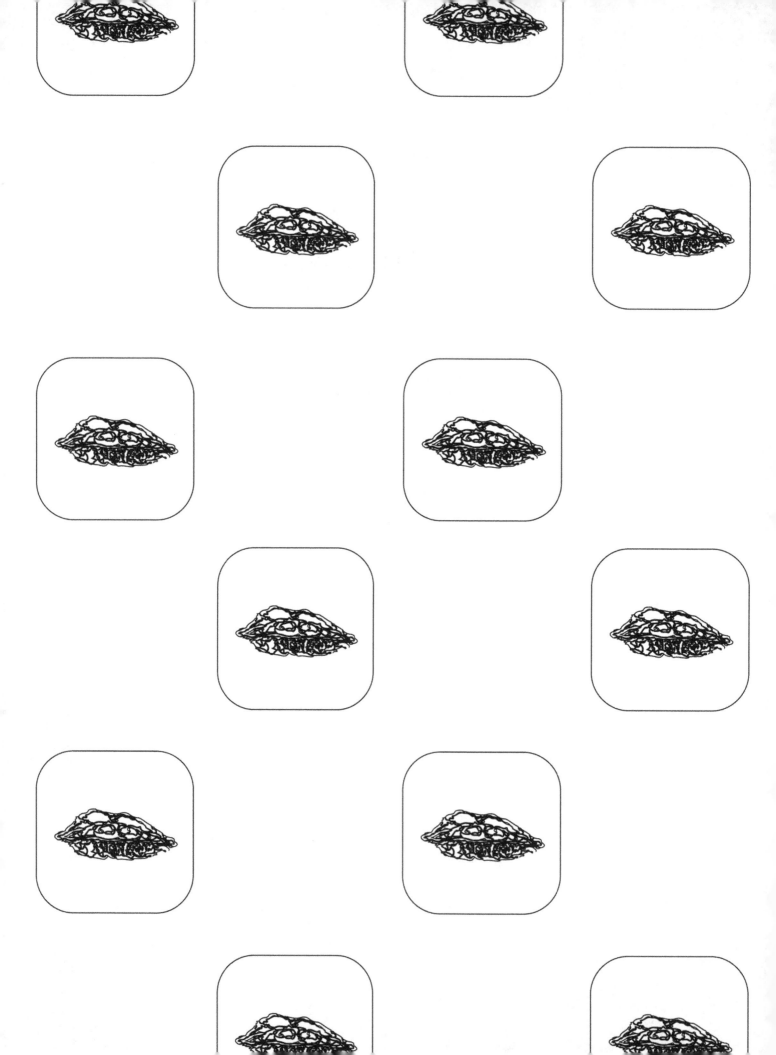

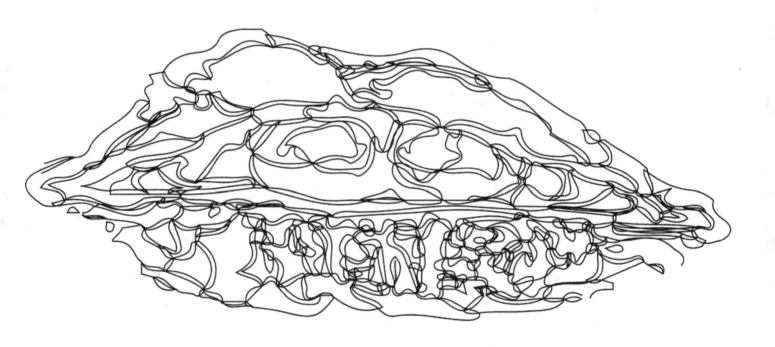

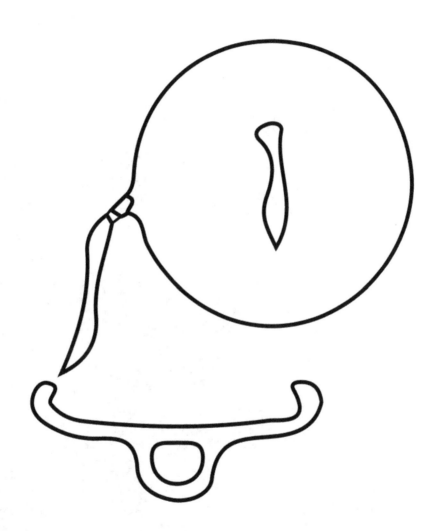

I believe

I believe

I believe

I believe

I believe

I believe

I believe

The smallest sprout shows
there is really no death,

And if ever there was
it led forward life,

and does not wait
at the end to arrest it,

And ceased the moment
life appeared.

CPSIA information can be obtained
at www.ICGtesting.com
Printed in the USA
JSHW011446030822
28820JS00005B/68